Being a Kid
Ain't Easy

Being a Kid Ain't Easy

Martha Gray Henderson

Abingdon
Nashville

BEING A KID AIN'T EASY

Copyright © 1977 by Abingdon

Library of Congress Cataloging in Publication Data

Henderson, Martha, 1945—
    Being a kid ain't easy.

    SUMMARY: Stories dealing with the real problems of
children emphasizing that God can help with solutions.
    1. Children's sermons. [1. Sermons] I. Title.
BV4315.H39   252'.53   77-2135

ISBN 0-687-02814-0

MANUFACTURED BY THE PARTHENON PRESS AT
NASHVILLE, TENNESSEE, UNITED STATES OF AMERICA

To
Jonathan and Angie,
My Own Kids

Contents

Preface

Being a Kid Ain't Easy was begun with the realization that the church plays a significant role in the mental health of its members, particularly children. Without meaning to, sometimes the church fosters ill health. In an attempt to guide children in the "right way to live," teachers present stories of "good" Bible characters doing "good" deeds and saying "good" things. Children do need these examples, but they have other needs as well. When they hear little or nothing about negative feelings such as anger, hate, and jealousy, they may wonder what is wrong with them.

Childhood is not the happy-go-lucky age adults seem to remember. Children experience rejection, embarrassment, and disappointment just as adults do. They are affected by family crises, and they hurt very deeply.

Working in a mental-health center, I found the storytelling technique to be a most effective tool in communicating with children. Through this method, a therapist guides children in dealing with problems by presenting their situation in story form with a solution. In the church, teachers and ministers can employ the same method to communicate positively with children in an attempt to prevent problems.

The church has two advantages over the mental-health center in working with children. First, therapists see children *after* problems have developed and have to go through a process of undoing before any progress is made, while the church sees children throughout their development. Second, the church offers belief in a higher power as part of its teaching. As children develop a relationship with God, they learn that they are persons of worth because God created them. And they

11

learn that God cares about them and is ready to help them through all their difficulties.

In this book, it is my intention to provide stories that may be used to communicate positively with children. I have included some stories that deal with real problems children face and ways they might find solutions to them. It is my hope that through these kinds of stories our churches can meet some of the emotional as well as spiritual needs of children in the church, helping them to realize that they are important and that God is always with them.

Further, it is my intention to remind parents and other adults that being a kid ain't easy.

Where Is God When I'm Afraid?

A sermon to help children realize that fears are normal and that God is always present to help them when they are afraid.

Have you ever been afraid?

There are things to make us afraid. We have a psalm in our Bible that says, "What time I am afraid, I will trust in thee." God tells us in many ways that he loves us and will take care of us. He wants us to trust him when we are afraid.

Hal used to become frightened when he heard a storm. And he had a reason to be. Last year a storm came one afternoon and tore his family's home down. They were not there, but Hal was afraid another storm might come sometime when they were home and hurt them.

One night Hal was awakened by the roar of the wind. When he looked up and saw the quick streaks of lightening racing across the sky, he pulled the covers over his head. He was afraid to get up and go to his parents' room, so he just lay there and started to cry. He remembered the psalm about trusting in God when we are afraid. Now that he thought about it, he wasn't sure what we do when we trust God. He had just learned that verse in Sunday school, but he had not really thought about it in relation to his fear of storms.

Hal began to pray. He told God he was afraid, and he asked God to help. Hal peeked out from under the cover and saw that the storm was still going on. God didn't take away the storm, he thought. Hal pushed the cover down a little and watched how the lightning seemed to make the whole sky white. It lit up his room so much, he could see his desk and the pictures on the wall. He was fascinated by the storm. He pushed the cover down farther, got out of bed, and walked to the window. He saw the big trees bending one way and then another as the wind blew. He saw a lawn chair bouncing across the ground, and he saw puddles of water forming from the heavy rain.

Suddenly Hal realized that he was no longer in bed with his head covered. He was actually standing close to the window watching the storm! God did answer his prayer. He helped Hal trust him. Hal said the Bible verse aloud: "What time I am afraid, I will trust in thee." He was glad he had learned it. He was glad he knew God would take care of him.

God knows that there will be times when we are afraid. That is why we have a verse to remind us that we can trust him.

Why Does God Let Bad Things Happen?

A sermon to help children realize that God has not promised to protect us from harm, but he has promised to be with us no matter what we go through. And God has the power to take the bad and turn it into good.

Rachel listened as her mother and daddy talked about the latest news. Last night a robber took some money from the service station down the street and tied old Mr. Reese and left him in a closet. He had to stay in the closet all night until someone went in that morning and found him.

As Rachel listened to her parents wonder what the world was coming to, she asked why God let bad things happen. "Mr. Reese is so nice, and he wouldn't hurt anybody," she added.

Rachel's mother and father could not think of anything to say. They really did not know why God let bad things happen.

"Rachel, since we can't answer your question, why don't we try to find something about it in the Bible?" Daddy suggested.

"Okay, I'll get mine," she said.

"I think I can help," her brother said. "We had a lesson about that in Sunday school a few weeks ago. It was about Job and why God let a lot of bad things happen to him." Jay hurried to his room to get his Sunday school book.

Returning to the family room, Rachel showed her parents a paper with music on it. "We learned this song a long time ago. It tells us that God will take care of all people. But God wasn't taking care of Mr. Reese last night, was he?"

"See here." Jay pointed to a page in his Sunday school book. "It says that God let the devil do bad things to Job to test him. That means God wanted to find out if Job would keep trusting him even though these terrible things were happening," Jay explained to his little sister.

Mother was busy looking through her Bible too. "I found a verse that says God will take care of us and give us the things we need. It's Luke 11:9-10."

Daddy found a verse he wanted to share too. "In Luke 12:4-7 God promises us that we don't need to be afraid of enemies that might hurt or kill us. God tells us how much he cares for the birds and then he promises us that he cares even more for us."

"Romans 8:28 is one of my favorite verses," Mother began. "'All things work together for good to them that love God.'"

"Maybe that's the answer we're looking for," Daddy suggested. "Do you remember last summer when we had our wreck in the truck? We thought it was the worst thing that could have happened. Jay, your leg was broken, our truck was badly damaged, and we knew there would be no vacation. When our truck was being repaired, we learned that there was a defective part in it that could have killed us if we had driven as far as we had planned. The wreck was bad, and we were all upset for several days, but as it turned out, that wreck may have saved our lives. God didn't protect us from having the wreck, but I know he was with us. And I believe that God was at work turning something bad into something good."

"Yes, and spending our vacation at home was a lot of fun," Mother reminded them. "I think we all agreed that it was our best."

When bad things happen to us, our families, and our friends, we wonder why a loving God allowed it. God did not promise to take away hurt, loneliness, and death, but he did promise to be with us no matter what happens. There will probably be times when we will not be able to understand why something

16

has occurred, but there will be other times when we, like Jay and Rachel's family, will be able to see clearly a blessing that might have been a tragedy.

Let's thank God that, no matter what happens, he will never leave us and that he has the power to turn bad into good.

Never Alone

A sermon to assure children that God never leaves them alone.

Louise looked around the room. She had never been in a hospital before, and she was scared. She wished her mother could stay with her, but she knew that was against the rules. Her mother had told her that the doctors and nurses would take good care of her and that both her parents would be there to visit every time they could.

Dr. Brown had explained why Louise had to have her tonsils removed. He also told her that she would be given a shot and then taken to a room where the operation would take place. Louise understood all of this, but she wished she did not have to be alone.

Louise heard a knock at the door and looked up to see Brother Allen, her pastor. Louise smiled. She liked him and was glad he had come to see her.

"You certainly do look healthy to be in a hospital," he said. "I remember when I had my tonsils removed. I was just about your age, and I was really scared."

Louise smiled. She wanted him to keep talking.

"I tried to tell my doctor that my tonsils were fine, and I was sure they didn't need to be removed."

Louise laughed. She had felt the same way, but she knew it would not do any good to try to convince her doctor she didn't need an operation.

"I didn't know what was going to happen in that operating room," Brother Allen continued. "All they would tell me was that it wouldn't hurt. My daddy was with me when the nurses came to get me for surgery. The last thing he said was,

'Remember that you are not alone. God is with you.' And that's what I came to tell you. Your mother and daddy can't be with you in that operating room, but God can. And he won't leave you alone."

Louise smiled as he took her hand. He held it tight and assured her he would be thinking about her. That meant a lot to a frightened little girl, but having him remind her that God would be with her all the way meant even more.

Brother Allen left, and the nurses came to take her to the operating room. Louise didn't feel alone any more.

Like Louise we can be glad that God never leaves us alone. Let's thank him now.

When You're Lost

A sermon to assure children that God is with them.

Wendy looked at the houses along the street. None of them seemed familiar. Wendy didn't know where she was. She had been playing at her friend's house just a few blocks from her home. She had been there many times before. But today, when it was time to go home, she saw some big trucks with bright decorations on the side. They were several blocks past her friend's house, but Wendy wanted to get a closer look. She knew the trucks were part of the circus that was coming to town for the week. She thought if she hurried to the corner she might be able to see some of the animals.

When she got to the street corner, the big trailers carrying lions and elephants were passing. Wendy was excited when some of the performers waved at her. She ran down the sidewalk beside the circus trucks and turned the next corner with them. Wait until she told her friends about this!

When Wendy stopped, she realized she was lost. She did not even know how to get back to her friend's house. She began to cry. Mother and Daddy had taught her that God was always with his people. Right now, she felt very much alone, but she asked God to help her get back home.

Then she turned around and started walking back the way she came. She could not remember which street she turned from; she had made several turns to keep up with the circus trucks. Somehow she didn't feel alone anymore, and she wasn't afraid. She was sure she would find the way home.

There will be times when each of us will feel as Wendy did. We will find ourselves in new places that we don't recognize, and we will feel terribly afraid and alone.

Wendy asked God to help her get home. I believe God did answer this prayer later, but first he helped Wendy in a way she did not even ask. He helped her stop being afraid. He let her know that she was not alone. Even when we have problems that have not been solved, it is a good feeling to know God is with us. And he always is.

When You Need a Night-Light

A sermon to help children know that God understands when we are afraid.

"You're a big boy," Mother told Steven. "You don't need to have a light on in your room all night. There's nothing to be afraid of."

That was easy for Mother to say, Steven thought. He didn't know why he was afraid, but he was. He felt like a baby every time his mother or daddy made some comment about his wanting a night-light in his room. It was bad enough that they kept talking about it in the family, but recently he had heard his mother telling some neighbors about it.

"I guess he's going to have to have a light on in his room when he goes to college," she had said.

And Steven's big brother had teased him in front of friends. That was even worse. Once Steven had tried to sleep without the light, but the next morning he was very tired because every time he had closed his eyes he became frightened, and he didn't get much sleep.

Steven wished that he did not get scared so easily. He felt stupid, and he wished his parents and brother would quit talking about it. In Bible school Steven learned a verse from Isaiah that said, "Fear not: for I am with thee." Steven's teacher told the children that the verse was a promise from God that he is with all of us, and we don't need to be afraid. That made Steven feel good. He had never thought about God being with him in his bedroom when he was afraid.

When Steven went to bed that night, he thought about what he had learned in Sunday school. He lay still after his mother turned the light off, and finally he went to sleep. During the night he woke up several times and was afraid. But each time he remembered that God was with him, and he went back to sleep.

The next morning, Steven was a little tired, but he was happy. He thanked God for being with him all through the night.

Sometimes mothers and fathers don't understand our fears. Even though they love us, if they don't understand our feelings, they can't always help. Sometimes we don't understand ourselves. But we can be sure at all times that God understands. He never laughs at our fears, and he is with us always.

God Answers a Prayer

A sermon to help children realize that parents cannot always help them. God understands and can help anytime.

Timothy walked out the door with his books in one hand and a piece of toast in the other. As he walked toward school, he thought how much he had wanted to talk to his parents about a problem he was having. One of the older boys at school had been picking on him every day, and he didn't know what to do. He had tried telling the teacher, but when she watched, nothing happened. Yesterday when he got home from school, his daddy was drinking. Timothy learned a long time ago that this was no time to try to talk to him or his mother. Mother was always mad at Daddy when he was drinking, and they usually argued a lot.

Timothy had wanted so much to tell his daddy that he had made the Little League team, but he knew Daddy would not be interested right now. He was finishing his toast as he neared school and saw Billy. He had a sick feeling in his stomach. He wanted to run, but he couldn't; he wanted to cry, but his daddy always told him that boys don't cry. There was nothing he could do. Just then the bell rang. Slowly Billy backed toward the doorway, watching Timothy every step. Then he turned to go to his room.

Timothy remembered that in Sunday school his teacher had told him that boys and girls could ask God to help them solve problems. Timothy knew God was pretty busy, and he wasn't sure that he had time for a little boy's problems, but he tried. As the class was beginning, he sat with his head buried in his spelling book. He was asking God to help him.

At recess, Timothy stayed close to the teachers on the

playground. Billy was watching him all the time, and Timothy was scared. He wished that God would hurry and do something. He wondered if God might make Billy's family move to another country or if he might answer his prayer by letting a teacher see how mean Billy was and make him stay inside for recess the rest of the year. He didn't know if God would answer at all.

After school, Timothy waited until Billy had gotten on his bus. He was glad that Billy had to ride a bus and he didn't. He waited until the bus was out of sight before he started walking.

"Hi, Timothy."

Timothy looked around to see Mr. Edwards raking leaves. Mr. Edwards was the Cub Scout leader, and Timothy could hardly wait until he was big enough to join. He liked Mr. and Mrs. Edwards very much.

"I heard you made the Little League team the other day. I'm proud of you," said Mr. Edwards.

"Thanks. " Timothy grinned.

Looking at his yard, Mr. Edwards laughed. "I've been so busy at work that I haven't had a chance to rake leaves. There are so many, I can't tell where my driveway is."

"I'm pretty good at raking leaves. Could I help?"

"That sounds too good to pass up. I pay fifty cents an hour. How is that?"

Timothy never thought about getting paid for raking leaves. He just liked being with Mr. Edwards, and he certainly didn't want to go home. He nodded. "I'll be back as soon as I take my books home."

It was fun working with Mr. Edwards. They talked a lot, and Timothy found that his friend was eager to listen to his problems. Mr. Edwards understood and made Timothy promise to come back and talk anytime he had a problem or just wanted to share good news.

Timothy learned a lot of things. He learned that there were

ways he could defend himself against Billy. He learned that it is all right for boys to cry. He learned that sometimes mothers and daddys have problems themselves that keep them from paying as much attention to their children as they should.

And he learned that God answers prayers of little boys.

Sometimes you might have a problem and find that you cannot get help from your parents. Just as Timothy did, you can ask God to help. We never know how he will answer, but we can be sure he will. Perhaps there is an older person in your neighborhood, a Sunday school teacher, or a friend's parents who might be willing to listen to you when you have a problem. Timothy found that God sometimes uses people around us to answer prayers.

When People Change

A sermon to help children find ways of dealing with situations they cannot change.

Wanda waved good-bye to her daddy as he left on another business trip. It seemed he was gone more and more, and she noticed that when he was home, the family didn't seem to have as much fun as they used to.

One day Wanda's mother wanted to have a talk. "Wanda, Daddy and I have talked a lot and have decided that it would be best for him to move to another city. You and I will stay here. Daddy will come back and visit often, and you may visit him when school is out."

Wanda stared for a few moments. "Are you and Daddy getting a divorce?" she asked.

Mother nodded and tried to explain.

After thinking about her mother's words, Wanda began to cry. She wished there were some way she could make her parents stay together. She wanted to talk to someone, but she knew her mother didn't feel like listening to her right now. Then she thought of her pastor. He likes to listen to children, she reminded herself. He told us so at church.

Mother was glad when Wanda asked to talk to Brother Adkins.

Wanda fought back the tears as she poured out her story to her pastor. Finally she asked, "Why don't they stay together?"

Brother Adkins began by reminding Wanda how she had changed over the past several years. "You don't like things you liked a few years ago. You even have different friends, don't you?"

Wanda nodded.

"All people change as they grow older," he continued. "When two people get married, they like each other the way they are then. Sometimes, though, when they grow older, they change in different ways. They may still like and respect each other, but when their ideas are very different, they may choose to go their separate ways. You know that they both still love you as much as ever, don't you?"

"Yes," Wanda answered.

"I know that you really want your parents to stay together, and, of course, you may still make that your prayer. But remember that God may choose to answer in a different way."

"How?" Wanda wanted to know.

"God may accept your parents' decision to separate. But he can still help you by showing you that you can adjust to the situation."

As they continued to talk, Wanda understood more. She was glad she had a pastor who was willing to listen to her. And she was glad to know that God can help us adjust to situations we cannot change.

We can be sure that when we are faced with problems we cannot resolve, God will help us find a way to accept them.

It Could Have Been Me

A sermon to help children understand and accept persons with developmental disabilities.

"Mom, may I play at Roger's today?"

"Bobby, you've been to his house several times recently. Why don't you invite Roger and your other friends here to play ball?" Mother asked.

"There isn't enough room."

"What do you mean? Your yard is bigger than Roger's."

Bobby looked away from his mother quickly. "Well . . . ," he searched for words. "We've already got our bases set up over there."

Mother sat on the sofa and motioned for Bobby to join her. "Is it because of your brother?" she asked.

Bobby was quiet for a few minutes. Then he nodded. "Roger and the other kids wouldn't understand about Billy. They don't know about being retarded. They would probably be scared of him or laugh."

"How do you feel about him?" Mother wanted to know.

"Gee, Mom, he's my twin brother. I understand him."

"It hurt Daddy and me a lot to know one of our children was retarded. We have all had to make some changes in our family life because of him. Sometimes it still isn't easy. But it isn't his fault that his brain is damaged. It isn't anyone's fault. It could have happened to any of us."

Bobby started to his room. On the way he saw Billy sitting on the floor of his room, playing with blocks. As he watched his brother, he thought about what his mother had said. That could have been me, he thought.

Slowly Bobby walked into Billy's room. "What are you doing?"

Billy smiled and made some noises, but the only word that could be understood was "blocks."

Bobby picked up some blocks and showed his brother how to stack them according to colors. Billy clapped his hands in delight. Then he tried to do it.

After a while, Bobby heard the telephone ring. When Mother called him, he ran to the phone.

"Hello, Roger. Hey, why don't you guys come over here to play ball? We could set up the bases in our backyard, and my brother could watch us."

Even though a loving God has created each of us, there are some who may not have healthy minds and bodies. Let's ask God to help us show understanding toward them.

Marsha and Rene

A sermon to help children look beyond the way others appear and accept the real persons.

Marsha and Rene stared at the new girl who had just been introduced to them. Sarah was wearing a faded blue dress, old socks, and a pair of shoes that looked as if they had been given many coats of polish to cover all the scuff marks.

"I wonder where *she* came from?" Marsha whispered to Rene as she straightened her new purple pantsuit.

"I hope she doesn't sit by us," Rene responded.

The teacher was taking time to let the students introduce themselves to Sarah. When Marsha and Rene told her their names, the new girl smiled warmly. She did not seem aware that her clothes were not as nice as those the other girls were wearing.

Sarah said little during the next two classes. When it was time for lunch she followed Marsha and Rene outside and sat near them under a tree. She listened as they complained about having to eat leftover steak and roast beef sandwiches, and she also noticed their frowns when they saw her peanut butter sandwich.

After lunch, Marsha and Rene took their places in English class. When they saw Sarah standing at the door, the girls looked away quickly so she wouldn't think they wanted her to sit by them.

Sarah seemed to understand. She chose a seat two aisles away and opened her book. Miss Bess, the English teacher, welcomed Sarah and explained that the class was studying creative writing.

31

"Were you doing any of that at the school you were attending?" she asked.

"A little," Sarah nodded.

"Very well. Class, I would like for all of you to get out a piece of paper and write a poem. You may choose the subject and style you wish. When you finish, we will begin reading them in class."

Marsha and Rene were among the first to read. They usually did well in this class, so they were eager to share what they had done and receive Miss Bess' praise. Miss Bess did praise them, but she also offered criticism that she felt would help the class.

Then it was Sarah's turn.

"I wonder if she's as dumb as she looks," Marsha whispered.

Sarah began reading so softly that Miss Bess had to stop her and ask her to begin again and speak louder.

Marsha and Rene giggled.

Finishing her poem, Sarah returned to her seat. Everyone was quiet.

"How did you like Sarah's poem?" Miss Bess asked the class.

"That was really good," one of the boys answered.

"I wish I could write like that," said a girl on the front row.

"It was beautiful, Sarah. It's good to have you in our class, and I look forward to hearing more of your work," Miss Bess said.

"How can someone who looks like she does write like that?" Marsha asked Rene.

"I don't know, but I liked it. We really don't know her. Maybe she's very different from the way she looks to us now. We may even like her."

The next day Marsha and Rene were assigned to a discussion group with Sarah. They learned that her parents had died when she was small. She had spent several years in foster homes and in a child-care center.

"Gosh, no mother or father," Marsha said to Rene. "I bet it's hard to make friends when you don't even get to stay with the same family all the time."

The girls were leaving school when they saw Sarah. Almost without thinking Marsha called to her, "Sarah, do you think you could come to my house tomorrow after school? Several of the girls from class will be there, and we're going to have a party. I'd like it if you could come."

Sarah smiled and nodded. "I'd like that too. See you tomorrow."

Like Marsha and Rene, we often decide we don't like people because they look or dress differently. God looks beyond the way we dress, and he loves us. Let's ask him to help us look for the real person too.

Different but Alike

A sermon to help children understand others who are different.

It was the first day of Vacation Bible School and almost time for class to begin. Miss Leland, the secretary, knocked at Mrs. James' door.

"This is Jimmy," she said as she ushered the little boy into the room.

"Hello, Jimmy. I am Mrs. James. I will be your teacher this week in Bible school."

Jimmy smiled and nodded his head. He knew some of the boys and girls in the room because he and his family occasionally attended this church.

Mrs. James began class by asking questions about a familiar Bible story. She noticed that Jimmy did not seem to be paying attention unless she was looking directly at him. Finally she read a verse from the Bible and asked him to tell the children what it meant. Jimmy stared at her for a moment and then slowly shook his head.

"He can't hear," one of the children said.

Mrs. James looked around to see who had spoken.

"He's deaf. He can only understand what you are saying if you look right at him," Curtis told her.

"Oh, I didn't know that." Looking back at Jimmy, she chose a simpler question and spoke the words clearly so he could see.

Jimmy knew what had happened. At that moment, he wished he were anywhere but in Bible school. He answered Mrs. James' question, then he put his head down.

The bell rang, and the children rushed to the playground. As Mrs. James prepared refreshments, she watched the girls taking

34

turns jumping rope. The boys, except for Jimmy, were playing baseball. When Don rushed past her, she asked why Jimmy wasn't playing.

"Since he can't hear, he probably can't play very well. He would never be able to hear anyone calling him for a play."

"I see."

When the children returned to the room, Mrs. James asked them to put their workbooks away. "We will go back to them in the morning, but right now, I have something else I want us to do."

Raising one hand in the air, she began moving her fingers as if exercising them. "Does anyone know what I'm doing?"

There were nine faces that looked puzzled, but one face was smiling.

"I think Jimmy knows. Would you tell the rest of the class?"

Jimmy held his hand up and repeated the finger movements his teacher had made. "Mrs. James was saying 'hello' in sign language," he said.

Writing the letters of the alphabet on the board, Mrs. James told the children that people who can't hear sometimes depend on a language they can see. "Let's learn to talk with our hands," she said.

With Jimmy's help, she showed the other children how to form each letter of the alphabet with one hand. They practiced spelling words, and then Mrs. James taught the class a song they could sing with their hands.

When the bell rang, the children moaned. They did not want to leave. Mrs. James was happy to see them so eager to learn. She was also happy to see the children walking close to Jimmy as he helped them with their signs.

The next morning, the class worked hard. At recess, Mrs. James watched the boys walk out with Jimmy. She smiled when she saw them talking to him—with their hands. They made him first baseman and found he played quite well. The boys laughed together because they were able to talk with their hands, baffling their opponents.

Before it was time to go home, Mrs. James asked the children if they had learned anything they would like to share.

"I have." Curtis raised his hand. "I learned that Jimmy is just like the rest of us. I thought I didn't like him at first, but that was because I didn't understand him. It was fun learning sign language, but it was even more fun making a new friend."

One of the hardest things we have to do is learn to accept people who are different. Everywhere we go we will find people with different colored skin, different languages, and perhaps handicaps that make them different. When the children in Jimmy's class got to know him, they realized he was more like them than different. Let's ask God to help us understand others too.

Judy Needs a Friend

A sermon to help children see others as individuals—creations of God.

"There's a new girl in my class," Michelle told her mother. "Her name is Judy. She seems lonely. She and her two brothers and their mother are living with some friends here, and it's very crowded. None of the other kids at school will play with them. Their mothers won't let them."

"I see," Mother said.

Michelle waited a few minutes for her mother to say more, but she didn't.

"Why won't Beverly and Jenny's mothers let them play with Judy?" Michelle asked.

"I know Judy must be lonely, Michelle. But her mother lives a different kind of life than your friends' mothers. The way she lives isn't good for children, and Beverly and Jenny's mothers want them to stay away. It's not that they don't like Judy. It's just better for you and your friends not to play with her."

"You mean I can't play with her either?"

Mother saw the look of surprise on Michelle's face. It was hard for her to explain because she had always told her daughter to be nice to all people.

"I think it would be better if you didn't," she finally said.

Michelle went outside and sat in her swing for a long time. She didn't really understand why her mother made such a decision, but she had found that even though she didn't understand, her parents were always doing the things they thought were best for her.

"Mother," Michelle was standing beside her mother in the kitchen now.

"Yes?"

"Judy is a very nice girl. If where her mother lives isn't good for children, maybe she doesn't like it either. Maybe she would like to come here and visit us. Do you think so?"

Mother didn't look at Michelle for a few moments. When she heard her ask again, she turned around to answer.

"I think that would be a good idea." Mother wasn't as sure as she sounded, but she told Michelle to invite Judy over.

Judy could hardly believe her ears when Michelle called. She would love to visit.

Mother learned that Judy was a very nice girl. And as the girls played together, she met Judy's mother and learned a lot about her too. She found that Judy's mother did not like the way she lived herself. She needed a friend. She needed to know someone cared about her. Michelle and her mother were glad they could be friends to this family.

Let us remember that all people are creations of God. And let us remember that the things God creates are good. There is a way we can share God's love with all people, even those whose life-styles are different from our own.

A Hard Decision to Make

A sermon to teach children that God wants us to share. It also points out the price of sharing.

There is a story in Matthew about a young man who had trouble making a decision. He told Jesus that he had kept all of the commandments, and now he wanted to know what else he needed to do. Jesus told him that he should give what he had to the poor. This made the man unhappy because he had a lot of things, and he didn't want to part with them. The Bible doesn't tell us what the man did, but we can understand how he felt.

Sharon was sad when she learned that her best friend had lost all of her clothes, toys, and books in a fire. She and her mother collected a box of food and clothing to take to Becky's family the next day. When they returned home, Sharon told her mother that she wanted to do something for Becky, but she didn't know what to do.

"If you were in Becky's place, what would you want?" her mother asked.

"Dolls," Sharon replied without hestitation. She was glad she had found the right answer, but then she wasn't so happy because giving Becky a doll meant she would have to give up one of her own. She liked all of her dolls, and she wasn't sure she wanted to part with any of them.

Sharon went to her room and looked at her dolls. When she thought about Becky with none, she decided to give her an old one that was missing an arm. Becky would be glad to get it since she didn't have anything, Sharon thought.

As she picked up the doll, Sharon did not feel happy about her decision. What if she were in Becky's place? Would she want someone's broken doll?

39

Returning the doll to the shelf, Sharon looked around the room again and spotted a doll that Becky always liked to play with when she visited. Sharon picked that doll up and held it close to her. It was not one of her favorites, but the thought of giving it up was almost painful. Finally Sharon decided that she wouldn't actually be giving it up by sharing it with Becky because she would still be able to play with it sometimes when she visited her friend.

Sharon took the doll downstairs and asked her mother to take her to Becky's house.

Let's ask God to help us find things we have that we can share with people who need help.

There's Something You Can Do

A sermon to help children realize that God can use them now.

Polly was walking home from a visit with her best friend when she noticed an old woman looking out the window of the big gray house on the corner. The woman waved when she saw Polly looking, so Polly returned the wave.

When she got home, she told her mother about the lady and asked who lived in the big house.

"That's Miss Edna," Mother answered. "She was sick when she was a little girl and has never been able to walk."

"You mean she just stays in that house all the time?"

"Most of the time. Occasionally some friends or relatives put her in a wheelchair and take her out when the weather is good, but the lady who takes care of her can't take her out by herself."

"She must be very lonely," Polly said aloud. "I guess that's why she sits by her window and waves at people."

"That's right," Mother said. "Friends go to visit Miss Edna as much as they can. She really loves to have company."

"Do you think she would like to have us visit her?" Polly asked with sudden enthusiasm.

"That's a good idea, Polly. Why don't we take her a bowl of fruit?"

"Okay." Polly clapped her hands.

Mother called Miss Edna on the telephone to find out when she and Polly could visit. Miss Edna was glad they were going to come.

The next afternoon, Polly met the short, gray-haired lady she had seen in the window. She was surprised to find a shut-in who seemed so happy.

Miss Edna talked to Polly's mother for a few minutes, then she turned to Polly. She wanted to know all about the things Polly liked to do, her friends, and her church.

She really seems interested in me, Polly thought. Then Polly started asking Miss Edna questions about herself. Miss Edna was pleased, and she told Polly about the books she liked to read and her favorite hobby—raising plants.

Soon it was time to go. Miss Edna thanked her visitors for coming and asked that they come again.

Miss Edna smiled. "Polly, I hope you will visit me often. It was such a joy to get to talk to you."

Polly felt happy about her visit. She certainly wanted to come again. I can take her a new plant, she thought.

Polly knew the women in her mother's auxiliary at church visited shut-ins and did nice things for people who needed help, but she had never thought that these were things children could do too. She was glad to find something she and her friends could do.

You don't have to wait until you are grown to do something for God. He can use you now.

Helping Without a Reward

A sermon to help children realize that God expects us to give without thinking about what we will receive in return.

Angie and Elizabeth were playing outside when they heard a noise from some bushes. The girls stood still for a few moments. Soon they saw something very small moving in the leaves. Bright red feathers appeared then were hidden again.

"It's a red bird," Angie whispered.

The girls walked closer. They saw the bird stumble and knew he was hurt.

"I'm going to take him home," Angie said, reaching for the crippled bird. "He will probably die if he stays here."

"Maybe we can help him get well." Elizabeth was enthusiastic.

"Yeah, and he can be our pet. Isn't he beautiful?"

The girls showed the injured bird to Angie's father and announced their plans.

"What can we do to help him get well, Daddy?"

"The best thing you can do is give him a good place to rest and plenty of food. The bird's wing will probably heal by itself."

For the next few days, the girls did not mind digging worms for their feathered friend. They gladly gave him all they could find. They gave him birdseed and kept a dish of water nearby.

"Look," Angie pointed excitedly. "Our bird is getting better. See how he's walking around now."

Elizabeth was happy too. The girls sat nearby while the red bird flapped his wings and took a few steps. The bird lifted off the ground and flew several feet away, then he rose again and flew high into the air.

Angie and Elizabeth stared in disbelief. Tears came to their eyes as they saw the red bird disappear in the distance. They could hardly believe the bird they had cared for had just flown off leaving them behind.

It makes us feel good to be able to help. We enjoy being able to do something for others when they are not able to help themselves. But often we think about the credit we expect to receive for helping. This is what Angie and Elizabeth were thinking about. They expected the bird to pay them back by being their pet, but the bird needed to be free, for that was the way he was born.

God wants us to be helpers. He wants us to give of ourselves, but he wants us to give without expecting a reward.

Sharing a Birthday Party

A sermon to encourage children to be sensitive to the needs of others and to share.

Larry watched the big truck drive away from the house across the street. He hoped there would be some children in the new family moving into the house. His best friend had just moved away, and he did not have anyone to play with. He had watched a bicycle being unloaded. There didn't seem to be many toys though. As a matter of fact, there really had not been a lot of furniture or anything moved.

Larry was playing in the front yard when an old brown car turned into the driveway across the street. He saw a woman take some small boxes inside, and then he saw a boy—just about his age, he thought—take a suitcase in. Larry wanted to meet the new boy, but he didn't know how.

"Why don't you invite him to your birthday party next week?" Mother suggested. "Then he would get a chance to meet other children his age."

"That's a good idea. Why don't we go over there now?"

"Okay." Mother had just baked some cookies to take to their new neighbors.

Larry met John and found out they would be in the same grade at school. Larry liked his new neighbor and was glad to be able to invite him to his house for a birthday party.

"The fourteenth?" John asked. "Your birthday is the fourteenth?"

"That's right. Saturday. And the party will start at three o'clock. Do you think you can come?"

"That's my birthday too." John said.

"Oh, then I guess you'll be having a birthday party yourself that day."

"No. But I'd like to come to yours."

Larry found out that John had never had a birthday party. He had only had a birthday cake once. His father had left home when John was a baby, so his mother had to work. She never had time for birthday parties.

Larry was still thinking about this when he and his mother got home. "Mother, what do you think about having two parties next Saturday?"

"What?"

Larry thought further. "I know! Let's have a surprise party for John at my party. We could put both names on the cake and tell everyone it's a double party. But John won't know."

Mother smiled. She was glad Larry thought of this. "I think that's a very good idea. I'll order a larger cake with both names on it."

Saturday came, and John was the first person to arrive. He carried a small gift in his hand. Larry thanked his friend and placed the package on the table. He hurried to the backyard with John so he wouldn't see the cake or the other children arriving with two gifts. After all the guests had arrived and John had met them, they went into the house. John stared at the mountain of presents. He had never seen anything like that. Then Larry's mother entered with a large yellow cake. There were candles on one side of the cake and more on the other. Then the group began singing "Happy Birthday." John was singing too until he heard them sing "Happy Birthday, John and Larry." His mouth opened, and he turned to his friend. All the children clapped their hands and shouted, "Surprise!" Larry's mother put the cake on the table, and John saw that his name was on it and that one set of candles was his. He waited for Larry to make a wish and blow out his candles. Then he made a wish and blew his out.

"What did you wish?" someone asked John.

"I wished that I would always have friends like you," he said as he looked at Larry.

All around us there are people who need friends. Larry realized John wanted a friend, and he found a way to be one. God can use us in a similar way if we will let him. Think of someone you know who might be longing for a kind word or deed from you.

Letters

A sermon to show children a way they can perform a Christian deed.

Do you like to get letters?

It makes us feel good to know someone is thinking about us.

Did you know that this part of the Bible is a group of letters one man wrote to his friends? *(Hold up the section of the Bible containing Paul's letters.)* Do any of you know the name of the man who wrote these letters?

It was Paul. Paul was a preacher who was born during the time of the New Testament. He went to other countries to tell people about God. As a matter of fact, Paul was the first missionary. When he had to leave one place to go to another country, he always took the time to write a letter to the friends he left behind.

Paul's letters might have looked something like ours. He began by greeting his friends and telling them where he was writing from. He always told them that he cared for them, and he let them know he thought of them often. He also said encouraging things to them and offered advice when he knew they needed help. He told his friends what he was doing and asked for their prayers. He always thanked them for their support.

Paul was grateful for his friends. His letters must have meant a lot to them. Do you suppose there are people now who would be grateful to receive a letter from you? Perhaps you have friends or relatives you have not written in a long time. It is always fun to write them. But what about people who do not get letters very often? Do you know any older people who live in nursing homes? What about sending a card to a sick person from your church or neighborhood? There is someone who would love to receive a letter from you. Perhaps you can think of someone.

Parents Have Problems Too

A sermon to help children realize that parents have problems that worry them and that sometimes children can help.

Kelly sat in her room thumbing through a book. She didn't understand what was wrong. Mother had had to cancel some plans she had made because Daddy had to go out of town on a business trip. This morning Mother was in a bad mood. She dropped three eggs, and while she was cleaning the floor, she burned the toast.

"What's wrong, Mom?" Kelly asked.

"Quit asking so many questions," Mother replied sternly.

"I only asked one."

"Well, be quiet and eat your breakfast."

Later Kelly heard Mother talking to a neighbor about how much it cost to raise children. I wonder if they wish they didn't have any children? Kelly thought. Mother and Daddy had always told her and her sister that they loved them very much. Maybe we're in the way now, though, she thought.

That night Mother came into the girls' room as she always did. She kissed each one on the cheek and tucked in their covers. "Remember that Daddy and I love you very much," she told them. "Sometimes we have a lot on our minds, and we may forget to tell you as much as we should," Mother said as she left the room.

Of course they still love us, Kelly thought. As she remembered the things that had been happening, she ran to her little sister's bed. "Maybe mothers and daddys have problems that worry them, and that's why they seem to be in a bad mood," Kelly told her little sister, who was almost asleep. "Maybe we are the ones who should be doing something to show them we love them. I know," Kelly continued. "We could polish Daddy's shoes for him, and we could clean the den for Mother."

The next day Mother went to the airport to get Daddy after his trip. When they returned home, they were quite surprised to see the work the girls had done. And on the table was a pretty arrangement of flowers with a note that said, "We love you."

Kelly realized that even adults have problems, and she found that there was something she and her sister could do to help. It means a lot to parents when their children do something nice just because they love them.

Maybe you can think of something you can do to show your parents you love them.

What's Right About Being Mad?

A sermon to help children realize that anger is normal and healthy and to show them that there are appropriate ways to handle this feeling.

Bobby put his bicycle in the garage, then went to the kitchen. He stared out the window while he ate a cookie.

"You're very quiet today," Mother said. "How was school?"

"Fine." Bobby finished his cookie and disappeared upstairs. After sitting in his room for a few minutes, he walked to the door of his brother's room. Ed had band practice that afternoon and wouldn't be home for a while.

Bobby entered the room and looked at the model airplanes, the books, and the rock collection. He felt so angry, he would like to tear up something that belonged to Ed, but deep down he knew that wouldn't really solve the problem.

On the way to school this morning, Ed had teased Bobby in front of some friends. He told them about something stupid Bobby had done last week. Everyone thought it was funny—everyone except Bobby. He had been mad all day. He tried to think of ways he could embarrass his brother in front of some of his friends. He knew it would probably be a long time before he got the chance to do that, and since he was mad right now, he wanted to do something right now. He decided it would serve his brother right if he took one of his airplanes apart or messed up his rock collection. Bobby reached for one of the airplanes and held it in front of him. Then he turned quickly when he heard someone behind him.

"Bobby, do you want to tell me what is bothering you?" Mother asked.

Bobby felt embarrassed that his mother had caught him. He felt as if she knew what he had been thinking. He put the airplane back and looked at the floor. He told his mother what had happened on the way to school.

"I know you must be pretty mad at Ed, and I don't blame you. Nobody likes to be embarrassed in front of his friends. But do you suppose there is some other way you could solve the problem?"

"What do you mean?"

"What would happen if you just told Ed you are mad at him?"

"I never thought about that."

"I don't think he meant to hurt you. He probably didn't even realize that he did. Maybe it would help if you let him know how you feel. It's up to you of course.

"You have to make your own decision, but remember that you are responsible for the decision you make. If you do something to hurt Ed just to get him back, then your daddy and I will have to deal with you as well as with him."

Mother left the room, and Bobby sat on his brother's bed for awhile. The back door slammed, and Bobby recognized his brother's footsteps. Walking to the top of the stairs, he called Ed.

Ed put his trumpet away and ran up the stairs. "What's up, Bob?" The door closed, and the two boys sat down to talk to each other.

All of us experience the feeling of anger, and although it is a normal and healthy feeling, the first impulse we have is to "get" the person we are angry with. But, as in Bobby's case, getting back at the person does not really solve the problem. There are healthy, appropriate ways to get rid of angry feelings.

Sometimes this can be done just by letting the other person know how we feel. We can be sure that God understands. He has given us the ability to have angry feelings as well as happy feelings, and he will help us find the best way to express them.

So You're Jealous

A sermon to help children realize that jealousy is a normal emotion and that there are ways to overcome it.

Cliff heard the doorbell ring. More people coming to see Cindy, he thought. For the past two weeks all of the neighbors had been coming to see his baby sister. Most of them brought gifts for her, and she wasn't even big enough to open them or care about them after they were opened.

Mother and Daddy had made it sound as if it were going to be great to have a new baby in the family. Cliff had been excited himself, but now he felt things were better before she arrived.

"How are you, Cliff? I know you are happy to have a little sister, aren't you?" Mrs. Oaks smiled as she patted Cliff on the head.

"Yes ma'am." Cliff knew he was supposed to be happy, so he always answered yes even though he really didn't feel like it. He sat on the front porch while several neighbors visited. He could hear them talking and laughing. Everyone said something about how cute his sister was.

It seemed to Cliff that nobody paid attention to him anymore. Daddy took him fishing yesterday, and next week the baby was going to stay with the grandparents while Mother, Daddy, and Cliff went to eat at his favorite restaurant. He knew he wasn't being ignored, but he still felt it was more fun before Cindy came.

That night when Cliff and his parents were saying their prayers, Cliff thanked God for his mother and daddy and said "amen."

"You didn't thank God for your sister," Mother noted. "You usually thank him for her."

Cliff unbuttoned a button on his pajama shirt, then buttoned it again. "I wish we didn't have her," he finally blurted.

"I know how you feel." Daddy put his arm around his son. "We've had to make a lot of changes since she came. And your mother and I have to give her a lot of attention."

"Just like we did when you were a baby," Mother added.

"I was just about your age when your Aunt Becky was born. I didn't like having a new baby around at all. I was jealous because I had to share attention with her. But you know, it's all right to feel jealous. As a matter of fact, it's pretty normal. It doesn't feel very good though, so we have to find a way to help us feel better."

"How?"

"Maybe you could help Mother take care of your sister or you could work some more on your rock collection or find some new hobbies. Mother and I still love you as much as ever. We always will. We'll help you, and remember that God will help you too if you ask him."

Cliff hugged his parents and got into bed. Again he thanked God for his parents, then he asked God to help him stop feeling jealous of his sister.

Many of you have brothers and sisters you have to share with. Sometimes you may feel that you are not getting any attention at all. This happens especially when someone else is sick and needs more care or when there is a birthday or other special occasion for another member of the family.

It is normal to feel jealous even though it is not a very good feeling. God is able to help us overcome jealousy and feel good about ourselves. Let's let him help us.

Big Empty Spaces

A sermon to assure children that God understands their grief and can help them.

Lisa sat on the steps of her new home and looked out at a neighborhood that seemed strange to her. The people even looked strange because she didn't know them. Lisa and her family had just moved to this new town and left behind all of their friends and all of the places that were so familiar. Lisa thought about her room in their old house, about her best friends, the park, the zoo, and all the good times she and her family had there. Lisa felt sad inside. As a matter of fact, she seemed to hurt all over. She felt as though she had a headache, a tummyache, and a pain in her side. Even her big toe hurt.

Now, Lisa is like every one of us. She had people and things she loved, and it hurt a lot when she had to be separated from them. Many of us misplace things and then feel a big hurt inside when we cannot find them. We lose friends when we or they move away. Some of us have lost friends and relatives through death, and that really hurts!

When you lose something or someone, it leaves a big empty space in your life. That is the way Lisa was feeling when she felt as if she hurt all over. Since she felt so bad, she decided to tell her parents. They understood, you see, because they were feeling the same way. They had some big empty spaces in their lives because they missed the friends and familiar places they had left behind.

As Lisa and her parents talked, she realized that she was still close to them. She also began to realize that when there are empty spaces in your life, you can find ways to fill them. When Lisa's parents asked her what she could do to fill some of her

57

empty spaces, she decided she could make some new friends. And Lisa was right. Her parents added that there were some new hobbies she could start and new places she could see. As Lisa thought about these ideas, she decided that this strange new town wasn't so strange after all.

Because we are God's children, he has given us feelings. We can be happy, we can feel sad and cry, we can feel frightened and angry. It is good to have feelings. When we lose something special we can, like Lisa, hurt all over. And also like Lisa, we can fill the empty spaces with new friends, new ideas, and new plans. God has given us the feelings, and he gives us ways to express them.

Four Eyes Are Better Than Two

A sermon that shows children that God is always ready to listen to them.

School was out. Mickey had the whole summer ahead of him to play baseball, go to the park, and visit with his friends. But after a few weeks of summer, Mickey didn't play baseball, go to the park, or visit with his friends. Whenever his parents asked what was wrong, he just answered that he would rather stay home.

Mickey's parents were worried about him, but they couldn't find out what was bothering him. One day Mrs. Ferguson walked into her son's room to put some clothes away. Mickey was sitting in front of his dresser staring into the mirror. He had taken his glasses off and was making faces into the mirror to see how he looked without them.

Mickey jumped when he heard his mother's voice, and he quickly put the glasses back on. Mother and Daddy had lectured him many times about taking his glasses off. They had explained that the glasses were expensive, and they would get lost or broken if he removed them.

"Mickey," Mother said as she sat on the side of the bed. "I didn't realize that your glasses bothered you so much. Is that why you have been staying home?"

Mickey began to cry. All he had heard the last two weeks of school was teasing. The other kids called him "Four Eyes."

"I don't ever want to go back to school." Mickey sobbed. "Please don't make me."

Mother reached out as Mickey ran into her arms.

"You mean there is another 'Four Eyes' in this house?" Daddy had heard part of the conversation from the next room.

He was smiling as he spoke. "That was my nickname when I was your age. I don't know if I want to share it or not."

Mickey stopped crying. "You mean it didn't bother you?"

"As a matter of fact it did. But when I realized they were only teasing, I decided to make them think it didn't bother me. So any time I heard somebody call 'Four Eyes' I would answer, 'Better to see you,' or 'Four eyes can see twice as well as two.' Do you know that it wasn't long until they quit teasing me?"

"Gee." Mickey smiled. Everything seemed so much better now. He couldn't wait to get his baseball and glove out and play with his friends. He wasn't going to let their teasing bother him. He was thankful for a daddy who understood.

It is good to have a father who understands. And all of us do. Even when our own parents may not understand how we feel, our heavenly Father always does. He can help us find answers to our problems, and he can help us accept our problems when there are no answers.

Someone Understands,
Even When Problems Are Small

A sermon to help children know that God understands even when their problems are small.

"Rise and shine. It's time for school." Mother sounded so cheerful, Sally thought. That's because she doesn't have to go to school, she guessed.

Mother pulled a pink dress with big patch pockets out of the closet. "How about wearing this today? You haven't worn it in a long time."

"I don't like to wear dresses to school." Sally protested. 'Nobody else wears dresses. Mother, why can't I get some old jeans like the other kids?"

"You have several pairs of slacks."

"Those are too dressy. I just want some plain old jeans."

"Slacks can be too dressy?" Mother questioned. "Too many sequins on them, I guess."

Sally did not appreciate her mother's teasing this morning. She felt out of place with her group of friends when she was the only one wearing a dress. The slacks she had were not much better, but her mother didn't seem to understand how she felt.

Sally put on the oldest pair of slacks she could find and gathered her books for school.

"You still couldn't talk her into getting you some old jeans, huh?" When Sally heard Mary's voice, she felt angry at her mother for making her go through the agony of being different from her friends. There was nothing worse, she thought, than having to look different.

Deep down inside she knew that wearing jeans was not the

most important issue her family faced, but it was important to her, and she wished someone would realize it.

Returning from school, Sally saw her mother driving in. Mother carried several sacks of groceries inside the house, then called to Sally to bring in a sack. The sack obviously didn't contain groceries. Sally was curious when her mother told her to open it. Then she smiled as she pulled out a pair of old, faded jeans.

"I was hurrying home so I could kick them around in the garden for a while." Mother was putting groceries away as she talked. "I wanted them to look as old and worn out as possible so you could look like your friends. Please wear a different shirt though, so I will be able to pick you out in a crowd."

Sally smiled. Her mother really did understand.

God has promised to help us whenever we ask. Sometimes the requests we make are important, but sometimes they may be very petty. Sally knew her request wasn't urgent, but looking like her friends was important to her. It made her feel good to know someone understood.

God is like that. He understands our needs, and he wants to help no matter how insignificant the problem may be.

Jill and the Chocolate Cupcakes

A sermon to help children realize that wanting honest praise for accomplishments is a human need and that God provides for that need.

Jill felt so big. She had helped her mother in the kitchen many times before, and today she was being allowed to make chocolate cupcakes all by herself. She was glad her mother trusted her to do such a big job alone.

Jill measured the ingredients as she had been taught and mixed them the way she had done many times before. She arranged the colorful paper baking cups in the muffin pan and poured the chocolate batter into them. She turned the oven on and placed the cupcakes on the top rack so she could watch them through the glass door. She didn't want to miss seeing them bake for even a minute.

Finally the cupcakes were ready. Jill couldn't wait to share them with her friends. She arranged several on a serving dish and took them across the street where several girls were playing. The cupcakes disappeared in a hurry, and everyone thought they were good. When Jill told them she had made them all by herself, they didn't believe her. One of her friend's older sisters even reprimanded her for telling something that wasn't true.

Running in the back door, Jill grabbed her mother around the waist and began crying. "They don't believe me," she sobbed. "Mother, go out there and tell them I *did* bake the cupcakes all by myself."

"It hurts when friends don't believe you, but we can't force them to believe even when we know we are telling the truth."

Just then Jill's daddy walked in. Hugging his daughter, he

wanted to know what she had been doing. Quickly Jill told him about the cupcakes she had made. Daddy sampled one and assured her it was the best he had ever tasted.

"You did a good job, and I'm proud of you," he added with another hug.

"Angie and Rene didn't believe I made them," she said. "Angie's sister even said I should be ashamed for saying I did." Jill poured out the whole story.

"Well, I believe you made them," Daddy said.

"I believe you made them too," Jonathan said as he grabbed one on his way through the kitchen. "They taste terrible."

Jill made a fist as if she were going to hit her brother. Then she smiled at her parents. "It wasn't terrible enough for him to quit eating, was it?" she asked. She and her brother liked to tease each other. And she knew he believed her too. Suddenly she realized something that was very important.

"I guess it doesn't matter as much that my friends don't believe me as long as my family does," Jill told her parents.

All of us need to feel that other people appreciate us and recognize our accomplishments. God gave us our abilities and wants us to use them, but he does not promise a lot of praise when we do. God understands our need, though, and in some way, he provides for it.

If No One Could See Me

A sermon to help children know that God cares about us even when we do things that are foolish. And God wants us to care about ourselves.

Did you ever wish that you were invisible? Do you think you would feel better sometimes if no one could see you? I have a story about a little boy who felt that way.

As Eric was leaving for school, his mother ran to the door waving his sweater. The sweater was a new one that his grandmother had knitted for him, but when he wore it to school, everyone laughed because it looked like a girl's sweater. Eric did not like the sweater from the beginning, but he thanked his grandmother as he had been taught. He had worn it to school only once, but that was enough. His mother just didn't understand why he didn't like it. Eric frowned as he took the sweater. He wished that he were invisible. If no one saw him, he wouldn't have to feel so bad about how he looked.

There were other times when Eric wished he were invisible. Last week the class was having a spelling bee. Eric was asked to spell a word that really wasn't difficult, but he missed it. He was embarrassed when he realized he had misspelled the word, but he felt worse when the teacher groaned and asked one of the better students to tutor him after class. As others in the class giggled, Eric wished he could disappear.

Eric was not a good baseball player, but he liked to try. Once the ball was coming directly at his bat, and everyone thought it was going to be a good hit. Eric swung with all his might—and missed the ball. Everyone laughed—that is, everyone but Eric. He felt more like crying. He wished that no one could see him.

Eric is not unusual. All of us feel like Eric sometimes. It hurts when we feel embarrassed. When we do and say things we think are stupid or when we feel we look silly, we begin to dislike ourselves. It is important for Eric and for us to know that in those awful times when we wish no one could see us, God is there and he cares just as much as ever. And what is more, God helps us forget the embarrassments we have. He helps us care about ourselves.

On Being Adopted

A sermon to teach children that God has created us, but loves us enough to give us freedom to make our own choices.

Russell wasn't sure how to take the news. His mother and father had just explained that he was their adopted son. This meant that they were not his natural parents. They received him after he was born and took him for their son. Then where were his real parents? he wondered.

"This means that you are extra special to us," his mother continued to explain, "because we chose you to be ours. You see, we wanted a little boy so much, and we asked God for one. Instead of letting one be born to us, he helped us find you. The first time we saw you, we were so excited. You were exactly what we wanted. You were our little boy."

"Who did I belong to when I was born?" Russell asked.

"We don't know them, but we know they loved you. They knew they could not be the kind of parents you needed, and since they cared so much for you, they decided to let someone else have you. I am glad for the decision they made even though it must have been hard for them."

"Why did they give me away if they loved me?"

"Do you remember the baby deer we found last fall?"
Russell nodded.

"Since the deer didn't have anybody to take care of him in the woods, we brought him home to help him. But you remember—when we talked about all the things a deer needs as it grows bigger, you knew you would not be able to take care of him. You made a wise decision to offer him to the zoo. Now that deer has grown pretty big, and you know you made the right decision. The deer could not have been happy or healthy living here, but he is happy at the zoo where he has a home much like the one he had in the woods. And he lives with other deer. It took a lot of courage for you to give up something you loved. It was because you loved the deer and wanted the best for him that you did give him up."

Russell knew the parents he had now loved him a lot. And although he really did not know his natural parents, he was glad to know that since they were unable to care for him, they loved him enough to allow other parents to have him.

In a way, this is what God has done. He created each one of us and loved us so much that he gave us up to make our own decisions. God wants us to be his—to be a part of the Christian family—but he does not force us.

As Russell found out, it takes a lot of love to give up something or someone you care about. Let's thank God that even though we are his by creation, he has made us free to choose to be his.

Rebuilding an Anthill

A sermon to help children understand how God has revealed himself to us.

Nathan watched carefully as Daddy started to pitch the ball. He gripped the bat and swung with all his strength. The ball disappeared into the vacant lot next door.

"Wow, that was a good one!" Daddy shouted as his son ran the imaginary bases. "I think it's about time for us to go in. How about helping me find that ball?"

Nathan smiled and hurried to catch his father. Together they kicked leaves and old limbs aside as they searched for the baseball.

Nathan swung his foot hard to move a large branch under a tree. Looking down he saw thousands of tiny ants scurrying in all directions. He noticed that he had knocked down an anthill—their home. Nathan kneeled down to watch the insects closer. He really felt bad about tearing up their home. He had not meant to do it. He took one hand and began pushing the dirt back the way it was. He wanted to rebuild the ants' home. They would like that, he thought.

Nathan moved back so the ants could go to their home. He did not understand why they were still rushing around as if they were trying to get away from the new home.

"I found the ball," Daddy said, tossing it in the air. "What are you doing?"

Nathan explained that he had tried to rebuild the ants' home. "But they won't go back to it. They're just running everywhere."

Daddy put his hand on Nathan's back. "That's because they don't know who you are. You are big, and you are different from them. You would have to become an ant yourself in order to let them know who you are and what you are doing. They only understand other ants."

As Nathan went into the house with his daddy he felt bad that he could not let the ants know he cared about them.

This story might remind us of a way God chose to communicate with us. God created us, but since God was not a person like you and me, his people on earth had some trouble understanding him. They did not know who he was. So God became man. He sent a part of himself to be human like you and me. That person was Jesus. It was easier for God's people to understand him when they were able to see and talk to Jesus.

When we read and talk about Jesus' days on earth, let us thank God that he loved us so much and wanted to send a part of himself down to help us understand.

Sam

A sermon to help children realize that God can help us overcome our guilt feelings.

"Remember to close the gate," Mother called.

Jeff had just gotten a new puppy, and his parents explained that they must always close the gate so Sam wouldn't run out into the street and get hit by a car. Jeff had a lot of trouble remembering, though, since there were good places to play on both sides of the fence, and he was always running from one to the other.

One morning Mother went outside to hang clothes. She noticed that the gate was open and Sam was gone.

"Jeff," Mother called. "Someone left the gate open, and Sam is out. We'll have to look for him."

"Oh no." Suddenly Jeff remembered that he had left it open last night. He felt terrible. He hurried to get on his bicycle and look for his dog.

"Sam, Sam," he called as he rode through the neighborhood. Oh, I hope he's okay, Jeff kept saying to himself.

Mother was looking in the woods behind the house. Just as she started back, she heard a soft noise. She stopped to try to find where it was coming from. Then she saw something black and fuzzy. It was Sam! But Sam wasn't moving. Mother could tell he was hurt. She threw the towel she carried over him and picked him up.

Daddy looked at Sam and called the veterinarian. Placing the dog in a carrier, Daddy left for the doctor's office.

When Jeff got home and heard about his pet, he cried, "He isn't going to die, is he?"

Mother didn't know. She just hugged Jeff and told him the doctor would do all he could to help Sam.

71

Jeff sat on the porch with his head resting on his hands. It was his fault that Sam was hurt, he thought. And if Sam died, it would be because of him.

Jeff looked up and saw his mother standing in the doorway. "We all make mistakes," she assured him. "It makes us feel bad to know we are responsible for someone else's hurt. We both know you didn't mean to leave the gate open. I'm sure you'll be more careful from now on, but that doesn't help the way you feel now, does it? Sam may be all right, but if he isn't, you'll have to accept it as something you can't change and learn from the experience. No one else will hold it against you, so you must not hold it against yourself."

Jeff still felt bad, but it made him feel better that his mother understood and had forgiven him.

We have a loving Father who is ready to forgive and forget our mistakes too. He understands the feelings of guilt we have when we do something wrong, so in addition to forgiving us, he helps us to forgive ourselves.

Patty's Secret

A sermon to help children realize that all people make mistakes, but God does not stop loving them. God is ready to forgive, and he helps us forgive ourselves.

Patty had a secret. She didn't want anyone to know her secret because it was about her—and it was bad. Patty did something once that she knew was wrong, and she was afraid that if her friends knew, they would not like her anymore. She had never even told her parents since she knew they would be disappointed, but now her secret was beginning to make her feel bad.

While a salesman was waiting on Patty's mother at the drugstore, Patty was walking up and down the aisles. She saw her favorite kind of candy and thought it looked better than it usually did. She really wanted it, but she had already spent her allowance and knew her mother would not give her any more money. She looked around the store and noticed that all of the salespeople were busy and didn't seem to know she was there. Quietly Patty took the candy and slid it into her pocket.

On the way home, she felt bad about what she had done, but there was nothing she could do about it now, she thought. At home, she went behind the garage and began eating the candy. It didn't look quite as good now, but she ate it any way.

Many days passed, and Patty kept thinking about what she had done. She thought about all of the times she had heard her parents and her Sunday school teachers tell her that taking something that doesn't belong to you is stealing. I'm a thief,

Patty thought one night as she lay in her bed. She was crying softly when she heard the door open.

"Patty, can you tell me what's wrong?" She heard Mother's voice in the darkness.

Patty's sobs became loud now as she grabbed her mother and buried her head in her chest. "I did something bad, and you aren't going to like me anymore," Patty managed to say.

"It might not be as bad as you think," her mother said as she held Patty lovingly.

Patty told her mother the story and then waited for a response.

"It is wrong to take things that don't belong to you, but that doesn't mean Daddy and I will stop loving you. If we quit loving one another because we made bad choices, I'm afraid no one would love anyone. When I was a little girl, I took some money from a neighbor's house. I found it on the floor when my mother and I were visiting. When we got home and I showed it to her, she made me take it back."

"But I can't take back the candy since I ate it," Patty said. "Is there anything I can do to make things right again."

"Yes, you can pay for it. You have some money in your piggy bank now. You can take it to the store and tell them what you did."

"I never thought about that," Patty said. She began shaking the money out of her bank and counting it. Placing the money on the dresser, she asked her mother to take her to the store the first thing in the morning. Then Patty kissed her mother good-night.

In the Bible, there are rules for us to live by, and as children of God we try to obey them. Sometimes, though, we make bad decisions. Patty learned that her own earthly parents were not going to stop loving her because she did something bad. God is like that. He is always ready to forgive. Furthermore he understands that sometimes it is hard for us to forgive ourselves. He is able to help us be forgiving. While we ask God to help us be strong and make good choices, let us also thank him that he understands and that he has the power to forgive us and help us forgive ourselves.

The Wrong Change

A sermon to encourage children to be honest.

Marilyn had five dollars to spend. She had been saving her allowance for a long time to buy a doll at Eldon's Gift Shop. Mother had promised to let her get the doll and pay the clerk by herself. She knew how much it would cost and how much change she should get, so Mother was going to wait in the car.

Marilyn took her time trying to decide whether to get the doll with the blond hair or the one with the brown hair. There were a lot of clothes to fit the doll, but she didn't have enough money for them. She selected the doll with the blonde hair and went to the front of the store. Marilyn took the money out of her purse and handed it to Mrs. Eldon.

When Mrs. Eldon handed Marilyn her change, she noticed that it was more money than she was supposed to have. She thought about the doll clothes she could buy with the extra money. She really did want them, and it would be a long time before she would have enough money from her allowance.

Marilyn knew her parents would not want her to keep the money since it did not belong to her. She remembered her father's saying that it was like stealing.

Marilyn pushed some of the money back across the counter.

"You gave me too much change, Mrs. Eldon," she said.

The old woman smiled. "Thank you. It makes me feel good to know there are honest people like you around. By the way, we have gotten a shipment of new products in that need to be unpacked. The girl who usually helps us is sick. Would you be interested in helping us while she is out?"

"And make money?" Marilyn asked.

"Sure."

"Wow, I would love to. I'll have to ask my parents, though." Marilyn hurried toward the door.

"Wait a minute. You forgot your doll."

"Oh yes," Marilyn laughed as she reached for it. "I'll be right back."

Marilyn returned with her mother. Mrs. Eldon told her, "We need someone who is honest, and I know Marilyn is."

Mother smiled. She would be glad for Marilyn to work.

Sometimes it takes a lot of courage to be honest. It would have been easy for Marilyn to keep the extra money. No one else would have known, and she would have been able to buy the doll clothes she wanted. But Marilyn's honesty prompted Mrs. Eldon to offer her a job, which was a better reward than the extra money would have been.

When we are honest, we may not be rewarded for it. Our honesty may not even be noticed by others. But we can be sure that when we are honest, God is pleased.

He Never Stops Loving

A sermon to help children know that God understands our weaknesses and is willing to forgive us.

Mother looked up just in time to see Kevin run through her flower garden. "Kevin, stop running over my flowers!"

Kevin continued playing outside. He had a new basketball and goal, and he spent a lot of time every day practicing. He bent his knees and eyed the goal. He gave the ball a strong push, and it went in. Kevin was so happy he threw the ball high into the air. When it came down, it fell in a lawn chair and scattered Mother's knitting.

"Uh oh," Kevin said aloud as Mother looked up.

"Kevin, please watch what you are doing," she said, frowning.

"I didn't mean to."

"I know you didn't, but you have to be more careful."

As Kevin listened to his mother, he remembered he had heard those same words earlier today. He had knocked his milk over when he reached for the salt at breakfast. He hadn't meant to make such a mess.

Yesterday Kevin had borrowed some of his daddy's tools to work in his tree house. He knew he was not supposed to use them alone, but Daddy had not been home, and he didn't want to wait. Daddy was very angry when he found one of his tools broken.

Kevin never meant to do all the damage he seemed to be doing. He knew what his parents expected of him, but sometimes he forgot. He always felt bad when he did something wrong, but of course by then it was too late. Kevin's parents were disappointed and sometimes angry when their son did not obey, but they never stopped loving him. Even when he was being disciplined, Kevin knew that beneath the feelings of the moment, there was a deep love that would continue.

God is like that. No matter how disappointed he may be, he never stops loving us. Even though he lets us know what he expects, he is willing to forgive us when we forget.

We can be glad we have someone who understands and loves us.

How many things can we do wrong — list them
are we still loved.

God loves us + forgives us forever

Katie and Sunshine

A sermon that assures children they are special just because God made them. No matter who they are or what they look like, they are loved.

Have you ever felt like no one loved you? It's a very lonely feeling. Today I have a story for you about a little kitten who felt just that way.

Scraggles was a little white kitten. He was very ugly. He had a crooked ear, a foot that turned out, and he was so skinny that when he walked, you could see his bones. When Scraggles was born, he and his four brothers and sisters were offered to anyone who wanted them. Scraggles watched hopefully as little children came with their parents to select a kitten. When the children saw him, they just commented on how skinny he was or how crooked his ear was. Finally Scraggles hid when people came around him.

One day he was walking down the street when three little girls appeared. He heard some giggles and looked up to see two of them pointing at him. Scraggles was surprised this time, though, because the third girl did not laugh. Before he could get away, he felt the little girl named Katie reach down and pat him on the head. Why, this really frightened him. This had never happened before, and he didn't know what to do.

Katie was now rubbing the kitten very gently and talking to him. What's going on? Scraggles wondered. This little girl actually seemed to care about him. Didn't she see his crooked ear, and didn't she notice how funny looking he was?

As Katie continued petting the ugly kitten, he began to snuggle up to her. Katie held Scraggles close and began walking home. Soon she was feeding him a delicious meal. She spent a lot of time taking care of her new kitten. As a matter of fact, when she gave him a bath, brushed him, and tied a blue ribbon around his neck, Scraggles forgot about being an ugly kitten. Katie started calling him her beautiful white kitten and named him Sunshine. This made him feel very good.

Sunshine was not lonely now. He was glad that someone cared enough to love him and to make him feel special.

As you know, that is exactly what God does. No matter who you are or what you look like, God loves you and is able to help you be the very best person you can be. Even if you limp, don't have nice clothes, or talk funny, you are special to him.

It's Okay to Fail

A sermon to help children realize that even when we do our best, things can go wrong. When we fail, God is still present to help us through the disappointment and to encourage us to try again.

David and Lynn hurried home from school because this was the day they were going to help their father plant the garden. He had set aside a special place for them to have their own garden, and he was ready to start the work when they arrived.

The children changed clothes quickly and ran outside to start making rows and plant tomatoes, corn, and pumpkins. They carefully followed their daddy's instructions, and soon it was time to water their new garden.

The children brushed some of the dirt off their clothes, then stood back and looked at their work. They were pleased because they knew they had done their best. Their father was proud of them too.

Every day they went out to look for tiny green plants peering up from the ground. They knew the tomatoes should come up first. They waited and waited and waited, but still there were no plants. It certainly was taking a long time, they thought. Finally the corn began to appear.

"The tomato seeds must have been bad," Daddy decided as he scratched around in the dirt where they were planted. "They should have come up a long time ago."

David and Lynn were disappointed, but they still had some corn and pumpkins to raise. They continued checking on the garden daily and making sure that the weeds were pulled out and the plants were watered.

At the end of the summer the pumpkins were getting bigger

and bigger, but something was happening to the corn. The children learned that it had been damaged by insects, and they would not be able to eat any of it. David and Lynn were very disappointed because they had done their best and failed.

"I'm never going to plant another garden," Lynn cried.

"I'm glad you didn't feel that way when you were learning to walk," Daddy said.

"What do you mean?" she asked.

"Well," Daddy began," when you were just a little girl, you pulled up to the big chair in the living room and tried to take some steps, but you toppled over and hit the floor. You were a little scared and mad, but you weren't about to let that stop you. The next day, you tried again and managed one step before you fell. You kept trying more every day until. . . . Well, look at you! You certainly aren't crawling around now. If you had gotten mad because you failed the first time you tried and had never tried again, look where you'd be—in a playpen." Daddy winked and started laughing. Lynn understood and smiled.

"I guess everybody has to fail sometime," she said. "Is it too late to plant something else?"

It is good to have someone who understands and is ready to offer encouragement when we fail. David and Lynn's father understood how disappointed they were after they had done their best and failed. Our own heavenly Father understands too, and he is always with us to encourage us to go on.

Honorable Mention

A sermon to help children realize that God expects us to give our best in the things we do.

Mark gave up baseball the third day in a row. He had found something that was more important to him. Each afternoon this week he had hurried in from school to work on a poster he was designing for an art contest.

Mark had always done well in his art classes, and he was the first person friends at church thought about when artwork was needed. When the contest was announced in his school, Mark got the support of all his friends and his parents. Everyone was sure he would be a winner.

Children throughout the county were invited to design a poster showing how boys and girls could be good citizens. Mark quickly thought of an idea and began working.

After many days' work, Mark put the finishing touches on his poster. He leaned it against a chair in his room and backed up to get a better look. He had had a lot of fun working on the poster, and he knew he had done his best. Since everyone else seemed to think he would be a winner, he began thinking it himself.

Mother drove Mark to an office where he submitted his poster. He could hardly wait until the winners' names were announced.

Finally the big day came. But Mark was not in first, second, or third place. He did receive honorable mention, but that seemed unimportant.

"You said you did your best," Mother said comfortingly. "For some reason the judges thought some other posters were better than yours."

"Just think of all the time I wasted on that old contest. I could have been playing baseball."

"Do you really think the time was wasted?" Mother stopped for a moment. "Are you sorry you entered the contest?"

Mark waited a while before answering. "I guess not. I did have fun, and I learned some things." Mark looked at his mother. "I liked getting to see what the other kids drew too. There were some good posters there."

"Did you know that the girl who won first place entered the contest last year and the year before without winning anything? She didn't even get an honorable mention."

Mark looked up in surprise. "Gee, I didn't know that. She did a good job. I bet she was really disappointed those first two years. I'm glad she didn't quit though. Her picture was better than mine, I guess."

Losing is a disappointment. So is making a bad grade or not getting the part you wanted in the school or church play. Disappointments hurt even more if we feel that we have done our best and that we deserve better than we have gotten.

God asks us to give our best to the tasks he has called us to do. That includes using the talents he has given us. He doesn't promise us we will be winners in the eyes of others, but we can be sure that when we do our best, he is pleased.

Who Has Talent?

A sermon assuring each child that God has blessed him with special abilities.

Angela took her turn washing the dishes while her sister Susan practiced piano. As Angela listened to the music flowing from the living room, she thought of how everyone she knew seemed to do something well. Her brother had won trophies for his performances in swimming meets, and her best friend Sally was always being praised for drawings she did. Then there was Jeanette. Jeanette seemed to be able to do everything well. It wasn't fair, Angela thought. She could sing and play the piano, she was good in sports, and she made better grades than anyone else in her class.

"I can't draw, I can't play the piano, and I do well to take a bath without drowning. I just can't do anything."

Angela remembered that her Sunday school teacher had said that God gives everyone talents and that he expects his people to use them. Unless mine is washing dishes, God must have missed me, she thought sarcastically.

The next day Angela was on her way to the store when she heard Jeanette's voice. Angela could almost feel a sharp pain going through her. It was bad enough to feel like a no-talent. Why did she have to run into someone like Jeanette who seemed to have more than her share? The two girls walked together and talked about school.

When they reached the corner, they saw a thin, white-haired woman working with her flowers.

"Hi, Mrs. Maberly," Angela called as the woman looked up. "Your flowers are beautiful." Mrs. Maberly walked to the fence and talked with the girls for a few minutes.

Angela and Jeanette hurried on their way until they heard the cries of a small child. Sitting on the curb was a little blond-haired boy named Timmy. Timmy had tried to tie his shoes and had gotten the strings in a knot. Since he didn't know how to solve the problem, he just cried.

"I used to get my shoestrings in knots every time I tried to tie them," Angela laughed as she helped Timmy. "As a matter of fact, I did it just a few days ago." Timmy brushed the tears off his cheek and smiled.

Before going into the store, Angela reached down to Sam, the Irish setter who lived behind the store with his owner. She stroked his fur gently.

Soon the girls were on their way home. Arriving at Angela's house, Jeanette said, "I wish I could be more like you, Angela."

"What?" Angela squealed in surprise.

"I mean you get along so well with everybody. I can't talk to older people. Little kids don't like me, and I'm scared of dogs. My mother says you are talented in that way. I'm not."

That's a talent? Angela questioned silently. I guess God didn't leave me out after all.

God did not leave Angela out, and he has not left any of us out. Each of us has the ability to do something well. Even if we do not know what it is now, we can be sure that God has given us a talent we can develop and use for him. He will help us find it at the right time. Let's thank him now for his gifts to us.

Don't Stop Dreaming

Children are sometimes reprimanded in school and at home for daydreaming even though they may make good grades and do their work well. This sermon is to assure children that it is all right to dream at times. Dreams can give them ideas that help them find out what they want to be and do.

Bobby could not help but jump up and down as he watched his first professional baseball game. He had seen so many games on television, and now he was actually in a stadium watching real live ballplayers. He tried to see every move. He noted the teamwork involved in playing a game, and deep down he imagined himself out on the diamond.

David had to go to school in his brother's hand-me-downs because his family was poor and could not afford new clothes for him. His parents never finished high school, and although they wanted David to, they never even considered the possibility of his going to college. When David told them he wanted to be a doctor, they told him to quit dreaming. They told him how much money it cost to go to school that long and let him know that they could not afford it.

Karen stared at the beautiful paintings hanging on the wall of the library. She studied each one carefully, especially the nature scenes. She liked to draw, but she knew she could not do anything as beautiful as the work she saw. Still, as she looked at the pictures and noticed the artists' names scribbled in the corners, she began to dream about seeing paintings with her own name on them, maybe on this same wall.

Marsha liked to swim. She had learned to swim earlier than most of the children she knew, and she could swim quite well. As she and her family watched the swimmers in the Olympics on television, she wished more than anything that she could someday be able to participate in that great event. She knew if she told her family about this dream, they would probably laugh. No one in her family had ever participated in any kind of competitive sports.

All of these children have dreams, just as you and I. God has given us our minds to think and dream. Did you know that the can opener, the refrigerator, the electric mixer, and all of the other things in your kitchen began as dreams? All of the inventions we have, all of the books that have been written, and all of the buildings that have been built started from dreams. The people we think of today who are famous were once boys and girls with dreams.

Whatever it is you want to be or do, keep thinking about it and do everything you can to work toward it. Study, practice, and work hard as you dream.

God has something for each of you to do. When you find a goal, don't stop dreaming and don't stop working toward it. God can help you achieve it.

What Happens When You Die?

A sermon to aquaint children with the reality of death but, more important, to make them aware of the joy of life.

Bobby walked out as the big doors of the hospital opened. Mother and Daddy were holding his hands on the way to the car. Yesterday he had visited his grandfather, but today the doctor said he couldn't. He waited at the nurses' station while his parents visited.

Yesterday Grandpa had been very tired, but he knew when Bobby walked into his room. He had moved his hand slowly to touch his grandson. When Bobby left with his parents, he heard his grandfather say, "You take care of your mom and dad for me." The old man smiled as his grandson nodded his head. Grandpa had been in bed a lot before going to the hospital. Bobby's parents had explained that he was old and would not be able to live much longer.

"What happens when you die?" Bobby asked as he climbed into the car.

"It means that you don't live on earth anymore. You go to a special place that God has planned. It is a place where people who are tired and sick won't have any more pain."

Mother added, "Grandpa has had a lot of fun in his life. He is happy that he has been healthy and able to live so long. But he is tired now and doesn't feel good any more. He knows it is time for him to go live with God. It makes us feel sad because we won't get to see him and talk to him, but we know that when he goes to be with God, he won't be tired and he won't hurt anymore. That is something we can be happy about."

"Jerry's mother told me he was sick today. Does that mean he's going to die?" Bobby wanted to know.

"No, Jerry only has a cold and can't come out and play until he gets well. We will all be sick sometimes, but that doesn't mean we are going to die. God made us, and the time will come when each of us will die, but usually it isn't until we get old."

"What is it like to go live with God?"

"No one knows. The Bible tells us that it is a place where people will be happy. There won't be any bad things happening, and no one will be hurting. God loves us, and I am sure that the place he has prepared for us will be good."

The time will come when all of us will lose someone we love through death. The time will also come when each of us will die. Bobby learned that even though there is sadness when someone we love dies, there is also cause for joy.

There is joy in being able to live on earth and there is joy in knowing that when this life is over, God has provided a place for us where there will be no sadness and no pain.

The Prize

A sermon to remind children that Jesus set the example of giving when he gave his own life for us.

All of the children were chattering when Miss Duncan entered the room. This was the day for the Easter egg hunt. Everyone had a basket filled with colored eggs.

When the eggs were collected in a large basket, three teachers went outside to begin hiding them. Miss Duncan led the children in some games while they waited for the eggs to be hidden.

"This year, we are not giving a prize for finding the most eggs," Miss Duncan told the children. "We do have a prize, but it will be given to someone you will help us decide on after the party today."

The children looked confused, but they were in a hurry to find eggs, so they rushed out without asking any questions. As she filled her basket, Patricia noticed that Amy had not found any eggs at all. She wanted to help her, but she didn't see any more herself. As Miss Duncan called the children to return to the room, Patricia quickly took three of the six eggs in her basket and gave them to Amy. Amy smiled at her friend as they walked in together.

After the children had counted their eggs and had eaten the refreshments, it was time for the prize to be given. Everyone was curious as Miss Duncan began reading a story about Easter. She reminded the children of the real meaning of Easter and how Jesus had loved us so much he gave his life for us.

"That is why our prize today is different. I want you to select someone you feel has shown the giving spirit of Easter to receive the prize. Think of someone who has done a kind act for someone else this morning."

92

"I think Patricia should get it," Amy said. Then she told the children about Patricia's giving her half of the eggs she had found. All of the children nodded their approval.

God has promised that he will not ask us to give more than we are able to give. We find giving difficult sometimes because we don't want to give up something ourselves. Jesus gave his life for us. Let's try to find ways that we can give of what we have to others.

A Day of New Hope

A sermon to make children aware of the meaning of Easter.

Have you ever gotten up so early in the morning that the sun had not even come up? Have you ever watched the sun rise?

A sunrise is always beautiful, and it has a lot of meaning for us. When the sun rises, it means a new day is beginning. It is a day of new hope, for it is full of opportunities, decisions to make, and life to enjoy. We can forget about the mistakes we made yesterday and begin all over today.

Today is Easter Sunday. It is a new day in two ways. First, it is a new day like any other—full of wonderful possibilities. But it is even more special. All of us know that this is the day we celebrate the resurrection of our Lord. Jesus loved us so much that he gave his own life for us. Even though he had not done anything wrong, he paid for the wrongs of all other people by dying. This was God's plan. But God's plan also shows us that death is not the end. Jesus rose from the dead and is alive now.

That is why this day is extra special. It is a new day, but it is also a day of new hope. Today we are reminded that because of Jesus' death and resurrection, there is new life for us after we die. The morning sun tells us about the beginning of a new day, but the morning sun on Easter reminds us we have a new life in Jesus.

This is a good time for us to thank God for the gift of life and for each new day we have.

Fifty-one Cents for Mother's Day

A sermon to honor Mother's Day.

Suzanne shook the pennies out of her piggy bank and began to count them. Forty-nine, fifty, fifty-one cents. What kind of Mother's Day gift can you get for fifty-one cents? she wondered. She put the money in her yellow purse and hurried to the car so she could go to the store with her mother. As her mother shopped, Suzanne looked at all of the things that were advertised especially for Mother's Day. She looked at the price tags and then at her little purse. There is nothing I can buy for fifty-one cents, and Mother's Day is tomorrow, she thought.

All the way home, Suzanne sat quietly looking out the window. What could she do? Last year she made a bouquet of tissue-paper flowers. Her mother seemed pleased even though Suzanne knew that they didn't look very good. The year before, her Sunday school teacher had helped all of the children make plaques for their mothers. Suzanne's mother still had hers among her most prized possessions.

Suzanne was in her room looking at books when she heard her mother's voice in the backyard. "I don't know when I'll ever get these flower beds weeded," she heard her mother say to a neighbor. "I have so much sewing that must be done now and the flowers will just have to wait. They do look a mess."

I know! Suzanne thought, I can *do* something for Mother's Day. That would be like a gift. I could weed Mother's flower beds for her present. I bet she would like that.

Hurriedly Suzanne took a piece of construction paper and cut it the size of a greeting card. She cut some pictures from old magazines and began writing a message to her mother. When she finished, she held the card up for her own inspection. On the outside were the words, Happy Mother's Day. On the inside was a picture of a little girl working in a flower bed. Above the picture, Suzanne had written, "A gift of love for the best mother in the world." Below the picture she wrote, "I promise to weed flower beds for a Mother's Day gift."

The next morning, Suzanne slipped the card under the edge of her mother's breakfast plate. Mother smiled as she sat down. Opening the card, her smile turned into a big grin. Mother pulled her daughter close to her. "This is the best Mother's Day gift you could give me. There is nothing I need more than to have someone pull weeds out of those flower beds. Thank you."

Suzanne was happy she had thought of this gift.

Since most boys and girls do not have a lot of money to buy gifts, perhaps you can, like Suzanne, think of something to do for your mother for Mother's Day. Your mother would probably agree with Suzanne's that there is nothing better than a gift of service, because you are really giving of yourself. And you are doing it because you love the person you are giving to.

Two Gifts for Father

A sermon to honor Father's Day.

Father's Day was three days away. Jeremy had wanted so much to be able to give his father something special this year. He knew his daddy would like to have a new fishing reel, but he had not been able to save enough money for one. He collected the money he had and made a list of the things he thought he could afford. Then he looked over the list and one by one marked off the things his daddy didn't need. All that was left was socks.

Jeremy took his money to the men's department of a store to look for a nice pair of socks. He spent a lot of time trying to decide which ones he thought his daddy would like best. Finally he selected the blue ones. When he got home, he carefully wrapped the present and hid it in one of his drawers.

Father's Day arrived, and Jeremy took the gift from its hiding place. While he was getting dressed for church, he heard the doorbell ring.

Downstairs, Daddy opened the door and saw an old man with a walking cane. "Mr. Adams? Are you Jeremy Adams' father?" the old man asked.

"Yes," Daddy replied.

"Two weeks ago I was leaving the supermarket when I dropped my wallet. Your son saw it, but he couldn't get my attention to tell me. He picked it up and brought it to my house. A lot of valuable papers and some money were in my wallet, and I can't tell you how grateful I am that an honest boy like yours found it. I forgot to ask him where he lived, and I've been trying these two weeks to find out so I could tell you how much I appreciate him. I would also like to give him this as a reward." The man handed Mr. Adams an envelope.

"Thank you for coming," Daddy said. Returning to the kitchen, Daddy took his place at the table and waited for Jeremy to come down.

"Pretend this is a new reel," Jeremy teased. "That's what I really wanted to get." He handed the gift to his daddy.

Daddy tore open the wrapping. Seeing the socks, he was quick to assure his son that they were exactly what he needed.

"This is the second present you've given me today, Son."

"What do you mean?"

Daddy handed Jeremy the envelope and told him about Mr. Jacob's visit. "That really made me proud of you. That's why I feel that I've received two gifts for Father's Day."

Daddy winked at Jeremy and added, "I really didn't need a new fishing reel anyway."

Seeing honesty in action is pleasing to the parents who have taught us to be honest. It is also pleasing to our heavenly Father.

Thanksgiving and Giving Thanks

A sermon to make children aware of the things God has given them.

"The turkey's gone. Somebody took the turkey. We can't have Thanksgiving without a turkey," Jerry was shouting.

Chaplain Moore laughed as he saw Randy racing across the stage with the cardboard turkey. "It looked so good, I had to sample it," he said, smacking his lips.

"Okay, boys and girls. We need to practice one time with our costumes. Tomorrow is the day for our big production, you know."

The children took their places quickly and began their lines. Robert was playing the part of an old Pilgrim who was one of the leaders in the trip to America. He knew the story well, and he was serious about the part he was playing.

Robert had just arrived at the Children's Home last month. His mother had died when he was very small, and last month his father became ill and could not take care of him any more. At the Children's Home, Robert found out there were some boys and girls whose parents did not want them. Others there had parents who, like Robert's father, were unable to take care of them. But now, all of the children had a place to live where a lot of people cared about them.

Robert liked going to school there. He had many friends, and not only did he get to play with them every day, but he got to live with them. It was almost like having a family with one hundred brothers and sisters!

After play rehearsal, the children gathered around Chaplain Moore. He was giving instructions about delivering Thanksgiving baskets. The children were divided into several groups, and each group was going to deliver a basket of food to a needy family.

Robert was in the group Chaplain Moore led. He helped carry the large basket as the group walked to a run-down house near the Children's Home. When they arrived, Robert saw several small children playing outside. It was cool, but none of them wore shoes and only one had a sweater. Chaplain Moore told his group that the father did construction work and usually did not get to work at all during the winter months. The family did not have much to eat, and there was little money to buy clothes.

When Chaplain Moore and his group reached the house, Mr. and Mrs. Smith came outside. They were grateful for the basket of food that they received. "This is a good Thanksgiving for us already," Mrs. Smith thanked the children.

As the children left the house, they talked about how little that family had. "Maybe we could find some shoes and coats for the children," Randy suggested.

"Yeah," replied Robert. "You know, it really makes me glad that we have such a nice home and family."

"I never thought of it like that, but you're right. We really are lucky."

Chaplain Moore smiled.

It's easy for us to notice all the things we don't have. We may even feel cheated when we are not able to buy some of the things our friends buy. But we don't often notice how much less some people have. Robert and his friends did not have a lot. They got new clothes only when they outgrew old ones, and most of the toys they shared belonged to all of the children at the Children's Home. Still they were able to realize that they had a lot to be thankful for when they met the Smith family.

Let's take time out this Thanksgiving season and notice all of the things we have, and let's give thanks to God.

Thank You for My Family

A sermon to help children appreciate their families.

A car stopped in front of the Brown's home. Jackie got out and waved good-bye to her friend. She had spent the afternoon with Amy at her new house. Amy used to live next door, but she had moved when her parents wanted to buy a larger house.

Jackie was helping her mother with supper as she described her friend's new house. "And all of the kids have their own bedrooms and bathrooms. They even have a playroom. You should see it!"

When Daddy got home, Jackie repeated her description of Amy's new house.

On Friday Amy was going to spend the night with Jackie. The girls would have to sleep in the den since Jackie shared a room with her younger sister. This had seemed like fun when she was planning it, but now as she thought about it, she didn't like having to move out of her room to have a friend visit. She wished their house were big enough for everyone to have a room.

Friday came, and Jackie was glad to see her friend. They played outside most of the time. The girls had fun helping with a cookout Jackie's mother planned. After supper Jackie and Amy began playing a new board game Amy had brought.

"That looks like a lot of fun," Daddy said. He sat beside the girls on the floor. "Would you let a couple of old-timers play?"

"Sure." Jackie moved over a little. "Amy and I will play you and Mom. You know you don't have a chance, don't you?"

Amy stared at her friend's parents. She couldn't believe they were going to play a game with them. Her parents never had time for playing games.

"It's getting late," Daddy announced. "It's time for Bible reading. And then to bed. And girls," he winked at them, "I want to hear a lot of snoring going on down here tonight."

Amy followed Jackie as the family sat at a table to read from the Bible. She joined with them as each said a prayer.

Soon the girls were in bed and the lights were out.

"Jackie, do your parents play games with you often?" Amy asked.

"Yeah, we do a lot of stuff like that."

"What about Bible reading? Do you do that every night? And have prayers together?"

"Yes. Doesn't your family?"

"No. We don't do anything together much. Mother went back to work so we could build our new house. When she gets in, she is always in a hurry to get the housework done. The only time I get to talk to her is when we are cleaning the house."

The girls talked until it was very late. But before going to sleep Jackie said another prayer. She thanked God for the house she had and for a family that liked to do things together.

Let's thank God for the times we share with our families. If your family doesn't spend much time together, perhaps you could suggest it.

Joy to the World

A sermon to celebrate the Christmas season.

Missy held tight to her daddy's hand as the crowds of people pushing by seemed to be trying to separate them. She had let go of his hand briefly in a store and felt herself being pushed against a counter. All she could see were mountains of brightly wrapped gifts. Tears had started running down her cheeks when she felt the warmth of her father's hand on her back. She quickly grabbed his hand and was determined that she would not lose him again.

As Missy and her father tried to weave a path through the crowds, she hummed softly with the records being played throughout the mall. "Joy to the World" was her favorite. She had learned that one last year in Sunday school. Her teacher had told the children that Christmas was the happiest season of the year because it was the time we celebrate Jesus' birth. All of the boys and girls had talked about the things their families did together at Christmas. Most of the children agreed that one of their favorite activities was getting to sing in the choir.

As Missy listened to the conversations around her, she wondered if these people did not like Christmas.

"I'll be glad when closing time comes. I've been on my feet all day."

"If that woman would decide what she wants, the line wouldn't be so long."

"I think I'll just get this for Aunt Ethel. She never gets me anything I like anyway."

Didn't these people know they were supposed to be happy? Missy thought. Just then, she heard a man's voice behind a door. "I've just about had it. If I had to work another day, I'd quit. At least fifteen kids stepped on my feet, four cried while they were sitting in my lap, and one pulled my beard. You can find another Santa Claus next year."

Missy's mouth dropped open as the man in the red suit walked past her and to the back of the store.

After supper, Missy told her mother and daddy what she had heard in the store. "Why aren't people happy?" she asked.

"People seem to be more interested in the presents they're getting and giving," Mother said. "Sometimes Daddy and I hurry around so much that we don't take time to appreciate the real meaning of Christmas ourselves."

Daddy thought for a moment, then asked, "What do you think we could do to celebrate Christmas this year?"

"Oh, let's go Christmas caroling!" Missy clapped her hands. Mother and Daddy looked at each other doubtfully. Since neither of them claimed to be singers, they weren't sure they wanted to walk down the street showing everyone how untalented they were. Then looking into Missy's eager face, Daddy winked. "Sounds like a good idea to me," he said. He saw Mother smiling.

Wrapped warmly in winter coats, Missy and her parents started their caroling in front of their neighbors' house. Missy saw Tom and Sally appear at the window. Quickly the front door opened and the children stood with their parents watching the three carolers.

"Why don't you join us?" Daddy invited.

"Yea!" Sally and Tom cheered as they ran for their coats. Their mother followed.

"Well, I was going to say no," Mr. Anderson laughed, "but I think I've been outvoted. I haven't been caroling since I was a boy anyway."

The carolers, now numbering seven, stopped in front of the next house to sing "Joy to the World." Missy thought everyone

104

looked happy. She listened to their voices blending, and she thought it was the most beautiful music in the world.

Maybe you and your family could find a special way to celebrate Christmas this year. Let's thank God for his Son and for this season.

A Birthday Cake for Jesus

A sermon to encourage children to find ways they can celebrate Christmas.

Christmas was only three weeks away. Diana and Sandra were getting excited. They had asked for bicycles this year, and they were sure Santa was going to bring them. But there was another occasion they were going to celebrate soon. Tomorrow was their birthday. They had selected the kind of cake they wanted, and they were going to help Mother bake it. The twins liked sharing a cake. They liked sharing a birthday too.

"Mrs. Gray told us in Sunday school that Christmas is Jesus' birthday."

"That's right," Mother said as she let the girls stir the batter.

"Then why don't we have a birthday cake for Jesus?" Sandra asked.

"Because Jesus isn't here, Silly," Diana laughed.

"Jesus isn't on earth, but he is alive," Mother said. "We celebrate his birthday in a different way. The music your choir is singing at church next week is a way of celebrating Jesus' birthday."

"Do we give presents to one another to celebrate his birthday?"

"I'm afraid that most of the time we don't think of it that way," Mother replied. "We like to give gifts to our family and friends, but sometimes we think more about what we are going to get from them, don't we?"

"You mean like bicycles?" the twins asked.

"Yes," Mother laughed. "Daddy and I think a lot about the things we are going to get too. It's fun to get presents, and we enjoy giving to the people who give to us, but I don't think that is really celebrating Jesus' birthday."

"Our Sunday school class is going to give a big box of things to a family that doesn't have much. That's celebrating Jesus' birthday, isn't it?"

"That's a very good way," said Mother. "That is giving willingly to people when you know they will not be giving to you in return."

"I don't think Mrs. Adams is going to have a very good Christmas this year," Sandra began. "She told us yesterday that her children and grandchildren lived far away and wouldn't be coming this year. She feels pretty bad about that."

"I wonder if there is another way you girls could celebrate Jesus' birthday?" Mother asked.

"What do you mean?" the twins asked together. Their eyes brightened as Mother suggested that the elderly lady next door might like to have some young visitors since her grandchildren would not be coming.

"Maybe we could take her some Christmas cookies or something!" Sandra shouted.

"We could make a present for her too," Diana added.

The girls were busy the next few weeks planning their surprise. Mother even invited Mrs. Adams over for Christmas dinner. On Christmas morning, the girls hurried to their neighbor's house to give her their gifts. When they returned home, they were surprised to see a big cake in the middle of the table. They had not even seen Mother baking. As they got closer, they noticed the writing. It said, "Happy Birthday, Jesus."

There are a lot of ways we can celebrate Jesus' birthday. See if you can think of some ways that will make Christmas have a special meaning for you.

Little Jobs Are Important

A sermon to help children realize that the little jobs they are called on to do are big responsibilities.

Ray had hurried to church for the Christmas play tryouts. He had read the part of Joseph over and over. That was the part he had hoped to play.

But Ray was not in a hurry to get home. He had not gotten the part of Joesph. He hadn't gotten a part *in* the play at all. The director had put him in charge of scenery.

"I think I'll tell him I can't do it," Ray told his mother.

"Why?" she asked.

"I wanted to be in the play. I didn't want the job of arranging scenery."

"There couldn't be a play without someone to take that job." his mother said.

"Well, someone else can do it."

"I guess it doesn't sound like a very important job, does it?"

Ray didn't say anything, but Mother knew that was the reason he didn't want the job. He had gone to tryouts with the hope of being the main character. Instead he had not even gotten a speaking part. Why, no one would even see him. All of his work would be backstage.

"That's the way it was for Jesus," Mother continued.

"What are you talking about?" Ray looked at her.

"When Jesus was born, he didn't seem very important to anyone. He didn't even rate high enough to have a bed to sleep in. Sleeping in a barn doesn't sound very good at all."

Ray was paying close attention to his mother. She didn't have to say any more. He knew that Jesus' job on earth was very important even though his life began without much attention.

The director of the church play had told all of the children that every job was important. The play could not be presented without the people backstage to take care of scenery, costumes, and lights. They were important even though they would never be seen.

When Ray had thought it over, he decided that he owed it to himself and the cast to do the very best job he could with the scenery. But most important, he owed it to God to do his best, even when the job was small.

Sometimes we feel hurt when the tasks we perform don't get attention. There are big jobs and little jobs, and they are all important. God wants us to give our best to whatever job we are called to do.

The Price of Freedom

A sermon to help children appreciate our country and freedom.

Most of us were born in this country and have lived here all of our lives. We call ourselves Americans. We have a home to live in, and we usually have plenty of food to eat and enough clothes to keep us warm when the weather is cold.

It would be hard for us to imagine the kind of life a child might live in some other part of the world. I have a story today about a little boy named Jody who lived in a country that was not free. In his country, the leaders told everyone what they could do and what they could not do. Even as a child, Jody had to work long hours in a factory with his parents. He was not allowed to play and have fun. All children and their parents had to work, and they didn't even receive any money for it. All Jody and his parents got was a dirty room to live in, a few clothes—not enough to keep them warm—and a little food each day.

Under these conditions Jody's father became sick and died. Since the leaders in this country were demanding more from the people all the time, Jody and his mother decided to leave.

Now, they couldn't just get on a bus or plane and go somewhere else. The leaders of the country would not allow that. Jody and his mother had to try to get out without getting caught. They walked many miles at night and hid in forest barns, and ditches during the day. They even rode unde hay in a farmer's hay wagon.

They were very tired and very much afraid. They di even get to eat every day. When they felt too tired to g they would stop and hear shots being fired around them.

110

knew if they were caught escaping they would be killed, so they started running again. Finally Jody and his mother were out of the country and free. But they still did not have a home or friends.

In this country that you and I live in, some people heard about Jody and his mother. They sent money for them to come to the United States, and they made a place for them to live. Jody finally got to play with other children, and he even got to go to school. His mother found a job she liked, and this time she earned money for her work.

Jody and his mother learned about the history of the United States, and they became citizens. But more important, they learned about God. They were sure God had helped them safely leave the country they were in. And they were sure God had led them to Christian friends and a new home.

When Jody sees the flag of the United States being raised, it has a special meaning for him. Silently he thanks God for this land and for being a part of it.

Maybe you haven't even taken the time to think about what living in a free land means. Let's consider the freedom we have today and thank God.